D1586310

INDIA ACTIVITY BOOK

Sonia Mehta

PUFFIN BOOKS

An imprint of Penguin Random House

PUFFIN BOOKS

USA | Canada | UK | Ireland | Australia | New Zealand | India | South Africa | China

Puffin Books is part of the Penguin Random House group of companies whose addresses can be found at global.penguinrandomhouse.com

Published by Penguin Random House India Pvt. Ltd
7th Floor, Infinity Tower C, DLF Cyber City,
Gurgaon 122 002, Haryana, India

First published in Puffin Books by Penguin Random House India 2019

Text, design and illustrations copyright © Quadrum Solutions Pvt. Ltd 2019
Series copyright © Penguin Random House India 2019

ISBN 9780143445289

Design and layout by Quadrum Solutions Pvt. Ltd
Printed at Aarvee Promotions, India

www.penguin.co.in

Hello Kids!

I discovered India because my father was in the Indian army. He was posted to many places all over India—and we dutifully followed him. By the time I was in the tenth standard, I had changed nine schools! Of course, it was hard making new friends almost every year, but the good part was that I got to live in so many different places. Right from Kerala, where I was born, to Kashmir, Jhansi, Shillong, Chandigarh, Goa . . . the list is long.

So I decided to write about India, its amazing history, its stunning geography, its millions of people and their traditions, and its diverse food, festivals and culture.

And then, I thought, why not have some fun and create some challenging activities and puzzles that are all to do with India? That's how this book came to be. It is packed with fun puzzles, activities and craft projects that will help you learn more and more about India as you work your way through them.

I do hope you enjoy this book as much as I have enjoyed creating it. I would love to hear from you. So do write to me at sonia.mehta@quadrumltdcom.

Lots of love,
Sonia Aunty

Mishki and Pushka have come to visit Earth from their home planet, Zoomba. They have never seen such an amazing place. Zoomba doesn't have trees and rivers and mountains like Earth does. But the people look exactly the same. On Earth, they meet a sweet old man whom they call Daadu Dolma. Daadu Dolma shows them around India and tells them about the history of each state, the languages people speak, the festivals they celebrate and the food they eat.

And now, Mishki and Pushka are ready to show off everything they know. **They can't wait to get started!**

Mishki

Mishki is a curious little girl. She always asks loads of questions. On her home planet, she is always getting into trouble for poking her nose into things that are not her business.

Pushka

Pushka is Mishki's brother. He loves adventure. He is always ready to try a new challenge. Whether it's climbing a mountain, or diving into a cold, cold sea, he is up for it all.

Daadu Dolma

Daadu Dolma is a wise old man who has lived on Earth longer than the mountains and seas. No one knows quite how old he is, but he certainly has been around. He knows everything about everything.

MAKE A MATCH

Can you match each state to its capital?

Maharashtra ● ● Jaipur

Gujarat ● ● Bhopal

Goa ● ● Kolkata

Rajasthan ● ● Dehradun

Uttarakhand ● ● Mumbai

Madhya Pradesh ● ● Panaji

West Bengal ● ● Gandhinagar

ROYAL TOUCH

The names of eight Indian monarchs are hidden in this grid. Can you find them? Look both horizontally and vertically.

C	H	A	N	D	R	A	G	U	P	T	A
S	D	B	W	E	R	S	W	E	R	T	K
R	T	U	D	C	F	H	X	C	B	B	B
B	G	R	H	R	J	O	W	S	A	D	A
S	D	F	G	H	T	K	C	F	B	G	R
X	M	S	H	I	V	A	J	I	U	Y	U
A	J	A	T	A	S	H	A	T	R	U	R
J	T	I	P	U	S	U	L	T	A	N	N
R	A	N	A	S	A	N	G	A	H	J	K

HIDE AND SEEK

Did you know that many English words have their roots in Sanskrit and Hindi? How many can you find in this jumble of words?

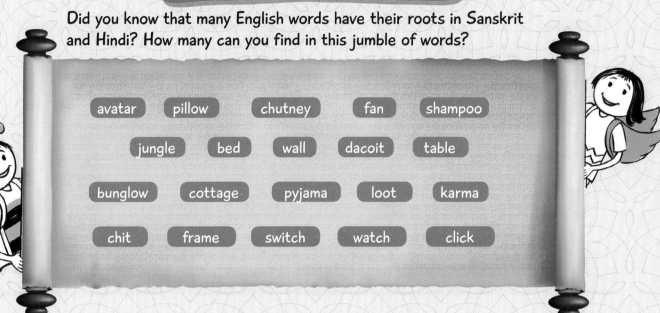

avatar   pillow   chutney   fan   shampoo

jungle   bed   wall   dacoit   table

bunglow   cottage   pyjama   loot   karma

chit   frame   switch   watch   click

UNMASKED

Chhau dancers from West Bengal wear masks like these when they perform. Can you find two identical masks?

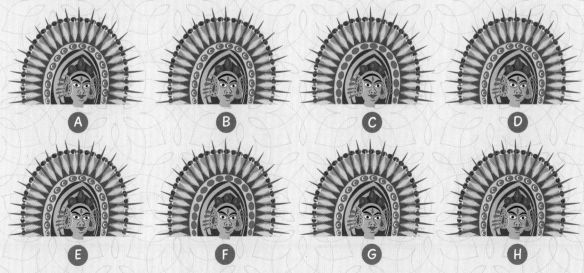

A   B   C   D

E   F   G   H

Here are six Indian monuments that are famous all over the world. Write down which city each can be found in.

1. Taj Mahal _____
2. Mahabalipuram _____
3. Gateway of India _____

4. Charminar _____
5. Qutb Minar _____
6. Cathedral of Bom Jesus _____

YUMMY MAZE

Daadu, Mishki and Pushka are hungry. Who's going to get to this yummy bowl of biryani first?

PICTURE MATCH

Draw a line connecting the name of the festival to the picture that represents it.

Diwali ●

Eid ●

Gudi padwa ●

Christmas ●

Bihu ●

FAMOUS FIVE

Here are five famous athletes whose names are scrambled. Can you unscramble them using the clues?

🔍 Athletic superstar
1. LIMAHK HNISG   ___ ___ ___ ___ ___   ___ ___ ___ ___ ___

🔍 Boxing champ
2. AYRM MKO   ___ ___ ___ ___   ___ ___ ___

🔍 Shooting star
3. VANIHBA ARDNIB ___ ___ ___ ___ ___ ___ ___   ___ ___ ___ ___ ___ ___

🔍 Cricket hero
4. HRULA VDIRAD   ___ ___ ___ ___ ___   ___ ___ ___ ___ ___

🔍 Female wrestling wonder
5. KASIHS LKIMA   ___ ___ ___ ___ ___   ___ ___ ___ ___ ___

STRUM AND HUM

How well do you know Indian music? Take the quiz to find out!

1. _____ is a melodious wind instrument that Pandit Hariprasad Chaurasia is an expert at playing.

   flute   trumpet   trombone

2. _____ is an enormous percussion instrument that people play during festivals and celebrations.

   nagara   tabla   mridangam

3. _____ is an instrument that is played at many Indian Hindu weddings.

   guitar   shehnai   tanpura

4. Ustad Zakir Hussain's instrument of choice is the _____.

   sitar   tabla   harmonium

5. An instrument that comprises ceramic or metal bowls filled with water

   _____.

   bul bul tarang   mast tarang   jal tarang

This dancer is performing Bharatanatyam, a dance form from Tamil Nadu. Can you find her exact shadow?

A   B   C   D   E

F   G   H   I   J

THAT'S ODD!

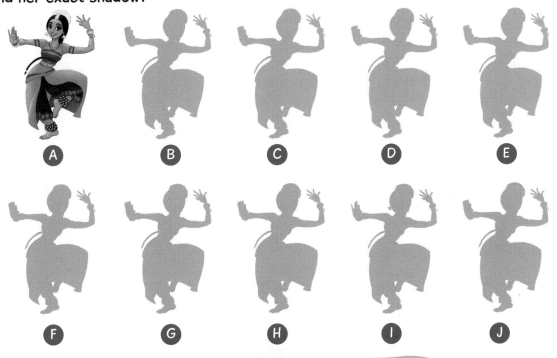

There's one word that doesn't belong in each row. Can you circle it?

sari	lungi	dhoti	pyjama
pagdi	pheta	cap	paag
kurta	kameez	shirt	jeans
jutti	paduka	belt	chappal
churidar	salwar	anarkali	jodhpurs

⋑ TORAN TIME ⋐

You have probably seen a string of flowers and leaves hanging above the doorway of many Indian homes. This is called a toran and it is a very old tradition indeed! People use different materials to make torans across the country: mango leaves are popular in the south, while fresh or artificial flowers and painted fabric are popular in the north. Here is how you can make your own toran to hang above your doorway.

You will need: crepe paper for flowers, twenty pipe cleaners, coloured ribbon

Here's what you need to do:

1. Cut up the coloured paper into 5X5 inch squares. Five squares will make one flower.

2. Make as many squares as you need depending on how many flowers you want to make (fifteen is a good number to aim for!).

3. Place five squares of paper on top of each other.

4. Fold all the paper squares together into an accordion or fan.

5. Twist the fan and attach to the pipe cleaner as shown in the image

6. Trim the edges of the paper to make petal shapes.

7. Now open out the 'petals' of the flower.

8. Repeat steps 3-7 to make more flowers.

9. String all the flowers together on the length of string or on coloured ribbon. Your toran is ready to be put up.

HELLO THERE

Can you circle all the words that express greetings in various Indian languages?

pranaam   paolee   vanakkam   namaste   yo

avishkar   nomoshkar   as-salam alaikum   bonjour

chamatkaar   kem cho   howdy   sat sri akaal   tambi

aadab   betaab   boudi   chewda   chaklee

namaskaram   hola   marhaba   ni hau

SMART CRAFT

India is full of the most amazing folk art and handicrafts. Match the name of the craft to the objects it is associated with.

Chanderi   paintings

Kolhapuri   toys

Madhubani   saris

Kondapalli   pottery

Sankheda   chappals

Khurja   furniture

RIVER CHASE

Reveal the names of five famous Indian rivers by filling in the empty boxes with the missing letters.

1. N __ __ M __ __ A

2. __ O __ __ __ __ I

3. K __ __ __ __ __ N A

4. Y __ __ __ __ A

5. __ H __ __ __ M

CRACK THE CODE

The name of one of India's many ancient empires is written in code below. Can you crack the code and find the name of the empire?

| 1 = A | 2 = Y | 3 = R | 5 = M | 6 = U |

| 5 1 6 3 2 1 |

TWIN DANCERS

These women from Rajasthan are performing the lovely ghoomar dance. Can you find two dancers who are exactly alike?

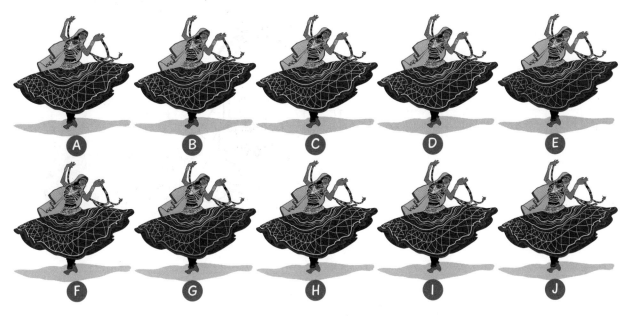

SOMETHING'S ODD

In each row, there's one famous Indian who doesn't belong there. Can you circle the name?

Sunil Gavaskar   Virat Kohli   Dilip Vengsarkar   Saina Nehwal   Chandu Borde

Rabindranath Tagore   Medha Patkar   Harivansh Rai Bachchan   Kabir Das   Mirza Ghalib

Yuvraj Singh   Ranveer Singh   Sushant Singh   Chitrangada Singh   Neetu Singh

Ratan Tata   Kumarmangalam Birla   Karan Johar   Mukesh Ambani   Rahul Bajaj

AR Rahman   Bhimsen Joshi   Raja Ravi Varma   Lata Mangeshkar   Kishore Kumar

PERFECT PALINDROME

The name of one Indian language is a palindrome—that means it is spelt the same backwards and forwards, like the words MADAM or CIVIC. Fill in the missing letters below to reveal the name of the language.

| M | | | | | | | | M |

PUPPET ON A STRING

Puppet making is a traditional Indian handicraft from Rajasthan. Can you spot eight differences between these two pictures of puppets?

MONARCH MATCH

Match each monument to the monarch it is associated with.

Gol Gumbaz

Ashoka Stambh

Gwalior Fort

Ashoka

Shivaji

Krishnaraja Wodeyar

Akbar

Sultan of Bijapur

Queen of Jhansi

Mysore Palace

Pratapgarh Fort

Agra Fort

HIDDEN FOOD

Rearrange the letters below to make the name of a delicious sweet treat made of yoghurt from Maharashtra. Do you know what it is?

H H N I K S A R D

☐ ☐ ☐ ☐ ☐ ☐ ☐ ☐ ☐

Follow the names of some of the festivals celebrated in India in this maze and trace a path to the end.

HIDDEN TRIBES

Can you find the names of seven Indian tribes hidden in the picture below?

MELODY MAKERS

Can you name these famous Indian musical instruments?

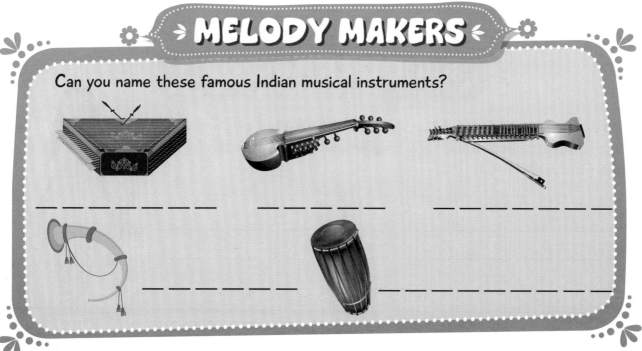

_ _ _ _ _ _ _ _ _ _ _ _ _ _ _ _ _ _ _ _ _

_ _ _ _ _ _ _ _ _ _ _ _ _

KATHAKALI MARVELS

One of these Kathakali dancers looks different from the rest. Can you spot which one?

A   B   C   D   E

F   G   H   I   J

HIDDEN WORD

An anarkali is a piece of Indian women's clothing that originated in the Mughal court. How many smaller words can you make from the word ANARKALI?

A N A R K A L I

_____ _____ _____ _____

_____ _____ _____ _____

_____ _____ _____ _____

_____

FARMER, WHAT DO YOU GROW?

The names of India's seven most widely grown crops are hidden in this grid. Can you find them?

```
C O T T O N A E D C
S M A I Z E F T Y U
E R T Y U I R I C E
Z X C V B A J R A V
R A G I A S D F G H
E D R J O W A R R T
W W H E A T C V F G
```

WHAT'S THE SYMBOL?

There are six national symbols of India hidden in this puzzle. Read the clues and fill in the boxes.

1. India's national bird.

2. India's national animal.

3. India's national flower

4. India's national fruit.

5. India's national game.

6. India's national tree.

NONSENSE WORDS

The names of five mountain ranges are hidden in these nonsense words.
Can you find them?

1. SAABHCYDAEDHRI _____
2. HXIMCABLAUYAPS _____
3. VCIBNYDIHOYPAS _____
4. ACRRATVNAOLLI _____
5. NUILPGIPRI _____

PERFECT RANGOLI

Here are four simple rangoli patterns for you to recreate. Choose the one you
like best. Draw it on a sheet of paper and colour it.

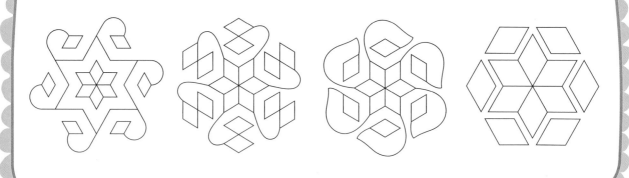

WARLI WONDER

The Warli tribe that lives mainly in Maharashtra is known for its distinctive art style. Follow the steps below to make a lovely wall hanging in the Warli style.

You will need: tissue paper, several sheets of newspaper, brown and white watercolour paint, glue, 1 thin rope

Here's what you need to do:

1. Mix the glue with water. Brush the newspaper with this mixture and place a layer of tissue paper on it. Let the sheet dry.

2. Then add another layer of tissue paper using the same method.

3. Thicken the newspaper by repeating steps 1 and 2 three more times. You will now have a thick, uneven board-like canvas.

4. Paint a layer of brown paint across the entire canvas. The idea is to make it look like rough mud. Let it dry.

5. Once it is dry, use the white paint to make a Warli-style painting. You may make any scene you want.

6. When your painting is totally dry, cut the edges of the canvas to even them out, if needed.

7. Then make two holes at the top, and run the rope through them. Your Warli-inspired wall hanging is ready to be put up.

FORT-I-FIED

Draw a line connecting each fort to the state it is in.

Gwalior Fort (it was used as a prison during the reign of the Mughals) ●

Golconda Fort (this fort is famous for its acoustics) ●

Pratapgarh Fort (this name means the 'Fort of Valour') ●

Chittorgarh Fort (this is said to be India's largest fort in terms of area) ●

Kangra Fort (this is one of the world's oldest forts and has been held by the Turks, Mughals, Sikhs, Gorkhas and British) ●

● Rajasthan

● Himachal Pradesh

● Madhya Pradesh

● Andhra Pradesh

● Maharashtra

FOODIE MAZE

Yummy! Find your way out of the maze by tracing a line connecting the names of foods below.

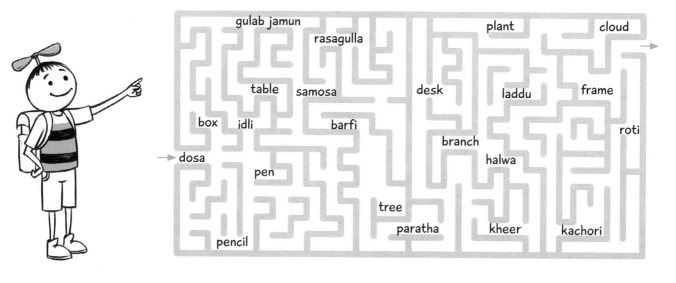

HAPPY HOLI-DAY

It's Holi and these children are having a wonderful time playing together. Can you spot ten differences between the two pictures?

ODD FOOD

In each row, there's one food item that doesn't belong. Can you circle the name?

jalebi	gulab jamun	kheer	upma	sheera
biryani	pulao	khichri	sevayian	bisi bele bhath
bhakri	chapati	dosa	rotla	paratha
bhel	jhal muri	chole-kulche	vada pav	puran poli
chutney	pachdi	achaar	kadhi	raita

TRIBAL TRACT

India is home to many different tribal groups. The names of some of these groups are hidden in the grid. Can you find them?

Angami
Banjara
Munda
Bhil
Asur
Warli
Jantia

```
A N G A M I A L E D
J W E R T M Y U I O
A A S D F U A S U R
N W W E R N W R F T
T S C V B D A D F G
I B A N J A R A B G
A D E T Y U L X C V
E R T Y B H I L E R
```

HIDDEN WORD

Here's a list of Indian musical instruments. But hidden in each word is another word for which there's a clue given alongside. Can you find the hidden word? One has been done for you.

The instrument	The clue	Your answer
1. Pakhavaj	A kind of Indian bread	Pav
2. Bulbultarang	Something that shines	
3. Mridangam	It holds back water	
4. Ghatam	You wear it on your head	
5. Dilruba	You do this to the lamp for the genie to come out	
6. Nadaswaram	What bees do when they collect together	

MISSING DANCER

Fill in the missing letters using the clue alongside each word as a guide. Then put the first letter of each word together to reveal the name of a famous Indian Kathak dancer, who has won many prestigious national awards.

1. ___ ___ ___ ___ ___ M (A state in northeast India)

2. I ___ D ___ ___ (A famous river from which India got its name—locally known as Sindhu)

3. ___ ___ ___ ___ ___ ___ ___ ___ U (A state in south India)

4. ___ H ___ ___ ___ ___ ___ ___ D (Previous state capital of Gujarat)

5. ___ ___ ___ ___ ___ ___ ___ ___ N (A desert state in India)

6. ___ S S ___ ___ (A state in northeast India)

7. ___ E ___ ___ ___ (India's capital city)

8. ___ L ___ ___ ___ ___ ___ ___ A (A set of caves near Mumbai that are named after an animal)

9. ___ I O ___ ___ ___ (A stringed instrument you play with a bow)

10. ___ ___ ___ ___ ___ (The world's largest democracy)

Famous Kathak Dancer:

THE CLOTHING JUMBLE

How many items of traditional Indian clothing can you find hidden below?

mundu	ghagra	mekhla	poncho	achkan	pagri	parka	jersey
sari	sarong	dirndl	socks	keds	panama	kilt
jeans	moccasins	dupatta	fedora	bow	sombrero	buckle
kameez	bloomers	beanie	cravat	dungrees	stetson	cloak

MISSING LETTERS

Choose the correct letters from the box to complete the words.

| CHUT | AVEL | RAMA | GOL | JHAR | ALU |

1. H ___ ___ ___ ___ I (A traditional family home in Rajasthan and Gujarat)

2. ___ ___ ___ ___ NEY (A spicy, green condiment that goes well with samosas!)

3. BENG ___ ___ ___ RU (The IT city in Karnataka)

4. ___ ___ ___ ___ YANA (One of the great Indian epics)

5. ___ ___ ___ CONDA (A place that was once famous for its diamond mines)

6. ___ ___ ___ ___ KHAND (The state that contains much of India's mineral wealth)

CODE CRACKERS

Can you crack the code and answer this question?

They came, they saw, they traded. What was their name?

| 2 = E | 5 = A | 6 = S | 0 = T | 1 = I | 3 = N | 8 = D | 7 = C |

| 4 = O | 10 = M | 13 = P | 12 = Y |

| 2 5 6 0 | 1 3 8 1 5 | 7 4 10 13 5 3 12 |

T H E ___ ___ ___ ___

___ ___ ___ ___ ___

___ ___ ___ ___ ___ ___ ___

WHAT'S IN A NAME?

Many of India's cities have been given new names since India became an independent country. Do you know the new names of these cities?

Bombay _MUMbai_   Calicut _Kobbckatta_

Trivandrum _thiruvanahthapnram_   Coorg _____

Baroda _____   Madras _chenni_

WILD AND WONDERFUL

Some amazing Indian creatures of the wild are hidden in this crossword. Can you find them?

Across

1. A kind of crocodile that has a similar same name in English and Hindi.
4. The lovely creature that is India's national animal.
6. A festival named after this bird is held in Nagaland.
8. A kind of deer that has another word for note hidden in it.
9. India's national bird.
10. A cow-like sea creature that lives around the Gulf of Kutch.

Down

2. The tallest of the wild cattle, found in Bandipur and other sanctuaries.
3. A one-horned creature that is Assam's pride.
5. An animal from the antelope family whose name literally means 'blue cow'.
7. A spotted creature whose snowy cousin lives in the mountains of north India.

HIDDEN WORD

KATHAKALI is a popular dance form from Kerala. It's also a really big word. Can you make ten smaller words from it?

K A T H A K A L I

_____   _____   _____   _____

_____   _____   _____   _____

_____   _____

HAPPILY MARRIED

Look at this happy couple from West Bengal who are all dressed up for their big day. Can you spot two couples who are exactly alike?

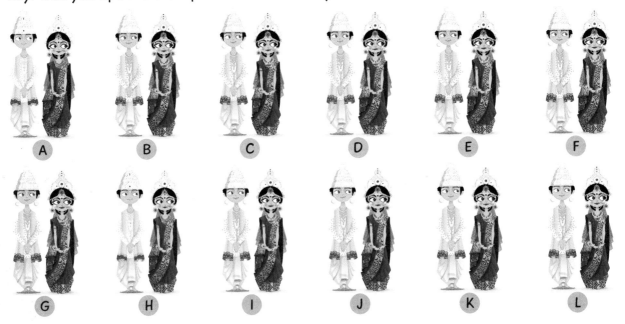

A   B   C   D   E   F

G   H   I   J   K   L

India has produced many fine authors. Fill in the missing letters to find the names of these five authors who have written books for children.

1. R _ _ _ _ _ N   B _ _ _ D (The man from the hills)

2. S _ _ _ _ A   M _ _ _ _ _ _ Y (The much-loved author and philanthropist from Bengaluru)

3. _ _ . _ _ .   N _ _ _ _ _ _ _ _ _ (He brought a village called Malgudi alive)

4. A _ _ _ _ T   P _ _ (We know him as the man behind Amar Chitra Katha)

5. S _ _ _ _ _ N   R _ _ _ _ _ _ _ E (Although he now lives abroad, he was born in Mumbai)

India has many beautiful wildlife sanctuaries. Some states are famous for the ones they are home to. Can you match the sanctuaries to the states they are found in?

1. Jim Corbett National Park ●   ● Assam

2. Ranthambore National Park ●   ● Karnataka

3. Kaziranga National Park ●   ● Uttarakhand

4. Bandipur National Park ●   ● Madhya Pradesh

5. Kanha National Park ●   ● West Bengal

6. Sunderbans National Park ●   ● Rajasthan

WHO DOESN'T LOVE A LADDOO?

Indian sweets come in a dizzying array of sizes, shapes and colours. Why don't you try your hand at making some simple coconut laddoos for the next special occasion you celebrate?

You will need: 3 tablespoons condensed milk, 4 tablespoons desiccated (dried) coconut, 2 tablespoons milk powder, 1 teaspoon raisins, 1 teaspoon crushed almonds

Here's what you need to do:

1. Mix all the ingredients together in a large bowl.

2. Once they are mixed, gently knead them into a dough.

3. Divide the dough into small, evenly sized portions.

4. Roll each section into small balls (you'll be able to make seven or eight, depending on the size)

Your laddoos are ready to be eaten!

THE HIDDEN EMPEROR

Fill in the boxes using the clues below. Then find the name of the emperor hidden in the yellow squares.

1. The second Mauryan emperor.
2. A famous ruler of the Gupta empire (his name has the Hindi word for sea in it).
3. The monument where the flag is hoisted and the prime minister makes a speech on Independence Day.
4. The 'Tiger of Mysore' who fought against the British.
5. The Greek king and warrior who launched an attack on India.
6. This maharani was believed to be one of the most beautiful women in the world, during her time.
7. The only empress to rule as part of the Delhi Sultanate.
8. They ruled Goa for many years.
9. What Mumbai was called? Before it was Mumbai, this was the city's name.

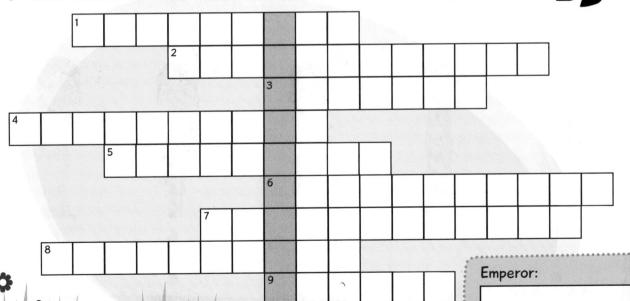

Emperor:

SPOT THEM ALL

Here is a picture featuring some famous Indian monuments. Can you identify at least six?

_____   _____

_____   _____

_____   _____

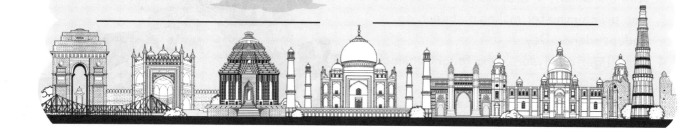

SARI STYLE

Did you know that the sari can be worn in lots of different ways? Here are some of the ways in which saris are draped in some Indian states. Match the drape to the state.

Maharashtra   Assam   West Bengal   Gujarat   Kerala

CELEBRITY SPOTTING

Do you know what these Indians were famous for? Tick the right answer.

1. Girish Karnad

cricket   swimming   writing

2. Dr Zakir Hussain

president of Actor's Association   president of India   president of Painter's Guild

3. Dr Salim Ali

archaeologist   ornithologist   psychologist

4. Dharmendra

doctor   actor   sculptor

5. M S Subbalakshmi

classical singer   classical dancer   classical violinist

HIDDEN INSIDE

Lepcha is the name of a well-known tribe from Sikkim. It's such a small word, but you can make more than ten words from it. Can you try?

LEPCHA

_____   _____   _____   _____   _____

_____   _____   _____   _____   _____

LET'S GO CLASSICAL

The names of eight classical dances of India are hidden in this puzzle. The letters in the yellow squares make up the name of a famous dancer. He was famous for merging Indian and western styles of dance. Can you solve the puzzle and find his name?

1. A dance that originated in Andhra Pradesh.
2. The dance of the state of Odisha.
3. A dance that originated in Assam that is associated with the Hindu god Krishna.
4. A dance that became popular in the courts of the Mughals.
5. One of India's most popular dances that comes from Tamil Nadu.
6. A dance form from Kerala for which the dancers' faces are heavily painted.
7. A dance form from Kerala that is known for its grace and beauty.
8. This dance is named for the state it originates from.

A   S   N

Famous dancer:

⇒ SYMBOLIC SUDOKU ⇐

This Sudoku is made of four objects that are Indian symbols. Can you fill in the missing squares, making sure that each symbol appears once in every row and column?

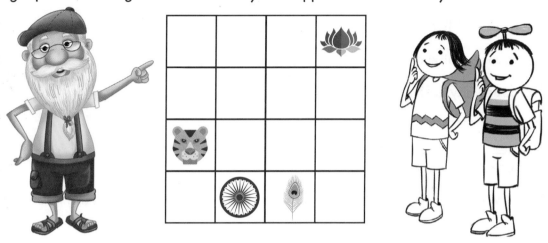

HIDDEN HORNBILLS

The hornbill lives in the Ghats and the Himalayas. How many hornbills can you spot in this picture?

FINDITABAD

There are many cities in India that end with the letters BAD. Can you fill in the blanks and find them all?

1. The capital of Telangana. ____ ____ ____ ____ ____ ____ bad

2. The former capital of Gujarat. ____ ____ ____ ____ ____ ____ bad

3. A crowded city in Haryana that's part of the National Capital Region. ____ ____ ____ ____ ____ ____bad

4. ____ ____ ____ ____ ____ ____ ____ ____ ____ bad. The twin city of another famous city in Telangana.

5. The city in Maharashtra near which the famous Ajanta and Ellora caves are located. ____ ____ ____ ____ ____ ____ ____ bad.

MUGHAL SPLENDOUR

This Mughal queen is enjoying her garden. Can you find eight differences between the two pictures?

LANGUAGE LILTS

Can you match the language to the state it is spoken in?

Bhojpuri ●   ● Goa

Telugu ●   ● Bihar

Konkani ●   ● Andhra Pradesh

Awadhi ●   ● Assam

Khasi ●   ● Uttar Pradesh

AMAZING ARTISTRY

Do you know which state these styles of embroidery and handicrafts belong to? Unscramble the words to find out.

ABDNHINA
from Gujarat

AABRESNI
from Benaras

_____

IULPKHRA
from Punjab

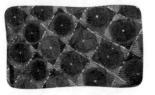

IATK
from Andhra
Pradesh

_____   _____

STANDING STRONG

Match the name of the monument to the type of monument it is.

Bhimbetka ●   ● temple

Mahabodhi ●   ● tomb

Gingee ●   ● palace

Humayun's ●   ● caves

Falaknuma ●   ● fort

RICE IS NICE

How many of these famous Indian dishes have rice as an ingredient in them?
Circle them.

idli   rasgulla   kheer   pani puri   dosa   khichri   korma

samosa   uttappam   pakoda   pulao   jalebi   biryani

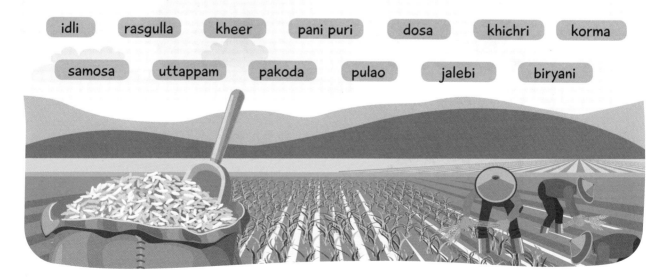

→ READY FOR A FEAST ←

This family is all set for a feast at the end of Ramzan. Do you know what the feast is called? Crack the code and find out.

| 2 = I | 3 = F | 5 = R | 4 = A | 8 = T |

| 2 | 3 | 8 | 4 | 5 |

____ ____ ____ ____ ____

→ MOVIE MAGIC ←

Can you find out the name of these classic movies?

1. A movie about a very important cricket match set during the British era _____

2. A Satyajit Ray classic for children about two fun characters whose names are in the title of the film. _____ _____ _____ _____

3. A famous movie about characters named Salim and Anarkali set in the Mughal Empire. _____

4. The first ever full length feature film to be made in India.
    _____ _____

5. A biopic about one of India's greatest athletes.
    _____ _____ _____

This autorickshaw driver looks happy. Can you find the exact shadow of his autorickshaw?

MAKING MUSIC

Rearrange the letters to find the name of an Indian string instrument used in West Bengal's folk music. Can you find it?

I H K A A C R

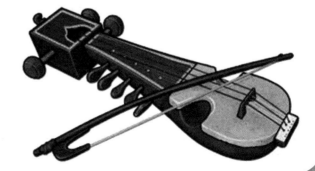

FOLKSY FUN

Every state in India has its own folk dance forms. Can you match each
of these folk dances to the state they are from?

Chholiya ●   ● Tripura

Hojagiri ●   ● Maharashtra

Karakattam ●   ● Uttarakhand

Lavni ●   ● Tamil Nadu

Dollu Kunitha ●   ● Karnataka

TRADITIONAL TRENDS

This Kashmiri couple is wearing traditional clothing. Can you find one couple that is
different from the others?

FISHING FUN

Fishing is a major source of income for people in coastal states like Goa, Kerala and Tamil Nadu. This Goan fisherman has cast four lines. Which line will catch the fish?

SOMETHING'S ODD

There's one animal that doesn't belong in each row. Can you circle it?

lion	tiger	snow leopard	rhinoceros
barasingha	chital	gaur	hangul
fruit bat	Indian peafowl	Indian pitta	satyr tragopa
gharial	speckled toad	mugger	Gangetic dolphin
iguana	king cobra	Indian mottled eel	banded krait

MINERAL MANIA

Some of the minerals found in India are hidden in this puzzle. Write the missing letters from the box in the blanks and complete the name of each mineral.

| COP | BAL | DIA | ANI | PHIT | MINI |

ALU ___ ___ ___ ___ UM

CO ___ ___ ___ T

___ ___ ___ PER

___ ___ ___ MOND

UR ___ ___ ___ UM

GRA ___ ___ ___ ___ E

A NATIONAL SYMBOL

Can you crack the code and find the name of the famous object that has found a place on the Indian flag?

| 1 = A | 3 = S | 8 = O | 7 = C | 9 = H | 6 = K | 4 = R |

1 3 9 8 6 1   7 9 1 6 4 1

LANGUAGE TRACK

Follow the track made by the languages of India and find your way from start to finish.

START

Gujarati	Russian	Chinese	Maghai	Malya	Yu	Vietnamese
Marathi	Konkani	Japanese	Romanian	Sinhala	Wu	Min Nan
English	Tamil	Urdu	Italisan	Thai	German	Hakkaq
French	Korean	Malayalam	Greek	Pashto	Arabic	Burmese
Swahili	Hebrew	Kannada	Maithili	Dutch	Portuguese	Sunda
Mandari	Polish	Thai	Sindhi	Punjabi	Turkish	Igbo
Spanish	Yoruba	Nepali	Hunan	Telugu	Sanskrit	Tagalog
Malay	Thai	Malay	Khmer	Javanese	Brajbhasha	Bangla

FINISH

JUTTI JOY

The colourful juttis of Punjab are well-known and much sought after. Can you spot ten differences between the two pictures of juttis?

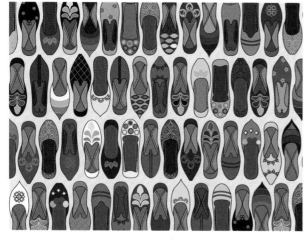
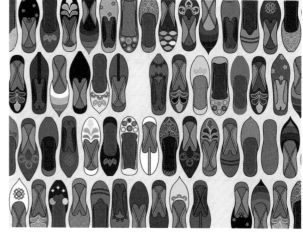

GUESS THE MONUMENT

India has some amazing monuments with incredible features. Can you use the clues to fill in the blanks?

1. It has an amazing whispering gallery. _____ _____

2. It has nearly a thousand windows through which breezes blow. _____ _____

3. It's the tallest monolithic (made of a single piece of rock) statue in the world.

   _____

4. It is one of the world's first astronomical observatories. There are five of them in India.

   _____ _____

5. An ancient gate to the old city of Delhi, this monument has a gory past and was used to display enemy corpses as a warning. _____ _____

SPICE IT UP

How well do you know your spices? Find the names of eight spices commonly used in Indian cooking.

```
A M U S T A R D V B
W S E D R C U M I N
S A F F R O N E R T
O T U R M E R I C T
F E N U G R E E K B
A S D F G C A R O M
V C L O V E W E R T
C I N N A M O N R F
```

CALENDAR YEAR

Can you arrange the following festivals in the order in which they appear during the year?

1. Independence Day
2. Navratri
3. Eid-Ul-Fitr
4. Makar Sankranti
5. Holi

6. Baisakhi
7. Republic Day
8. Dussehra
9. Christmas
10. Diwali

1. _____
2. _____
3. _____
4. _____
5. _____

6. _____
7. _____
8. _____
9. _____
10. _____

EPIC ANSWERS

How well do you know your epics? Use the clues to solve this crossword.

Across
5. One of Rama's twin sons
7. The sleepy brother of the evil king of Lanka
8. Rama's second twin son

Down
1. Rama's wife
2. The evil king of Lanka
3. Rama's father and the king of Ayodhya
4. Rama's loyal monkey supporter
6. Rama's nasty step-mother who banished him

This Sumi tribe from Nagaland is celebrating the Tuluni festival with a dance. Can you spot ten differences in the two pictures?

RAGA RAP

A raga is a set of rules on how to build a particular melody. It defines the order in which notes are to be played. There are hundreds of ragas that have been composed by great musicians through the centuries.

Which of these is the name of a raga? Circle those words.

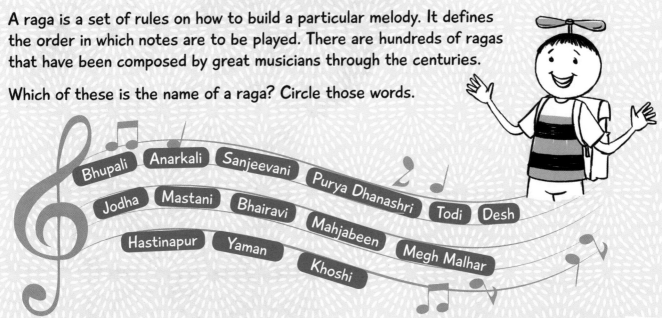

Bhupali Anarkali Sanjeevani Purya Dhanashri Todi Desh

Jodha Mastani Bhairavi Mahjabeen

Hastinapur Yaman Megh Malhar

Khoshi

TIE-AND-DYE T-SHIRT

Tie-and-dye or bandhani is a very popular method of dying fabric in Gujarat and Rajasthan. You can try it too.

You will need: old white t-shirt, rubber bands, fabric dye, large plastic bowl

Here's what you need to do:

1. Scrunch up parts of your t-shirt and knot them up using the rubber bands.

2. Empty the dye into the plastic tub or bowl. Make sure it is deep enough so that the entire t-shirt can be submerged in it.

3. Submerge your knotted t-shirt into the dye for about ten minutes

4. Remove the t-shirt from the tub and hang it up to dry in the sun. Hang it on a hanger so it gets air.

5. Once the t-shirt is dry, remove the rubber bands carefully. You will see that the dye has created an interesting pattern on your t-shirt!

Tip: You could even fold the t-shirt into different folds and then dip it in the dye. You'll find a different pattern emerging.

DABBA DELIGHT

The dabbawallas of Mumbai are famous all over the world for their incredible organizational skills. They deliver food to offices across the city in the most efficient way possible and they never make a mistake. Here are eight dabbawallas. Which one is different?

MUSICAL BEATS

What instruments are these musicians playing?

_____ _____ _____ _____ _____

ROOT OF THE MATTER

Many English words have been borrowed from Indian languages. Can you trace the words to their roots?

catamaran	gunny	opal	bandicoot

upala	pandikokku	katumaram	goni

SETTING A RECORD

Here are some of India's record breakers. Can you unscramble the words to reveal them?

The largest glacier in India is the ___ ___ ___C___ ___ N.

The highest rainfall in India is at M ___W S___ ___R ___M.

The coldest place in India is D___ ___ ___ in Ladakh.

The longest river in India is the ___ ___ ___ ___ ___S.

The smallest state by area in India is ___ O ___ .

The most populous state in India is
___T___ ___ ___ ___ ___ ___ D ___ ___ ___ .

WONDER WRAP

The name of a lovely kind of shawl made in Kashmir is hidden in this puzzle. Trace the letters to find it?

START

P	W	E	R	T
A	S	T	Y	U
R	H	M	I	H
D	F	G	N	A

FINISH

_____

OH WOW!

Here are some amazing facts about India. Solve this crossword and find out. Then, in the green boxes, you will find the name of a man from ancient India who was known as 'the father of plastic surgery'.

1. A game we all still play, that was said to have been invented in India.

2. A system of natural medicine that originates in India.

3. One of the world's first proper universities.

4. He was known as the 'Indian father of medicine' as he first put together cures using natural herbs.

5. A stream of mathematics that originated in India.

6. A set of practices aimed at keeping the body and the mind healthy that originated in ancient India.

Father of plastic surgery

[_____]

51

SORT IT OUT

There are fifteen monuments hidden in this word train. Can you sort them out and find them all?

SHANIVAARVAADAQUTBMINARJAMAMASJIDIRONPILLARELLORA
CAVESKHAJURAHOCAVESAGRAFORTLALMAHALBAHAITEMPLESAFDARJU
NGTOMBJAHAZMAHALBIDARFORTBIBIKAMAQBARA

_____   _____   _____

_____   _____   _____

_____   _____   _____

_____

ONAM FEAST

The feast served during the festival of Onam in Kerala is called a sadhya. Look at the treats laid out. Can you find ten differences between the two pictures?

ATONEMENT

An important festival that Jewish people celebrate as a day of atonement is hidden in this puzzle. Can you find it?

O P P K I Y M U R

☐ ☐ ☐ ☐ ☐ ☐ ☐ ☐ ☐

PAINTER PERFECT

There are nine Indian artists whose paintings are world famous hidden in this jumble of names. Can you circle them?

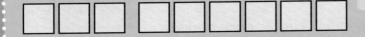

Lata Mangeshkar   Milkha Singh   Ratan Tata

M F Hussain   Ranveer Singh   S H Raza

A R Rahman   Sunil Gavaskar   Badri Narayan

Raja Ravi Verma   Baichung Bhutia   Tyeb Mehta

Amrita Shergill   Manjit Bawa   Anjolie Ela Menon

Akbar Padamsee   Mukesh Ambani

AMAZING!

Some amazing facts about India are right here in this puzzle. Match the columns to get the facts right.

Kumbh Mela ●   ● has the highest cricket ground in the world.

Rann of Kutch ●   ● was gifted to a Portuguese princess as part of her dowry.

Khari Baoli ●   ● is the world's largest gathering of people.

Chail ●   ● is where the pink flamingos visit

Mumbai ●   ● is the world's largest spice market.

WILD MAZE

There are two fun facts about India's wildlife hidden in this maze. If you are on the right track, you will discover some amazing facts.

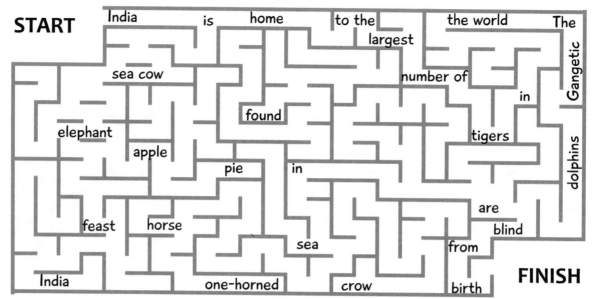

START

India   is   home   to the   the world   The

largest

Gangetic

sea cow

number of

in

found

tigers

elephant

apple

pie   in

dolphins

are

blind

feast   horse

sea

from

India   one-horned   crow   birth

FINISH

Can you match these names to the topographical features they are associated with?

Deccan ●   ● Abu

Mount ●   ● Desert

Rann ●   ● Bengal

Thar ●   ● Valley

Arabian ●   ● of Kutch

Bay of ●   ● Plateau

Silent ●   ● Sea

PRIME PUZZLE

Can you follow the path along the names of India's prime ministers?

START

Jawaharlal Nehru	Sunil Gavaskar	Sarojini Naidu	Lalu Prasad Yadav	Dhirubhai Ambani
Lal Bahadur Shastri	Rabindranath Tagore	Annie Besant	Sharad Pawar	Sam Manekshaw
Morarji Desai	Indira Gandhi	Rajiv Gandhi	M F Hussain	Amartya Sen
Satyajit Ray	Vallabh Bhai Patel	Narasimha Rao	Atal Bihari Vajpayee	Manmohan Singh
Raja Ram Mohan Roy	Mahatma Gandhi	Sonia Gandhi	Amitabh Bachchan	Narendra Modi

FINISH

A MONUMENT TO REMEMBER

Many generations of royalty are buried in this famous collection of tombs. What is its name?

Hint: Every alternate letter might just be unnecessary

QAUBTRBU   TSYHWADHYIW   RTYOQMCBVSM   _____

STREET TREAT

The names of eleven yummy Indian street food dishes are hidden in this grid. Find them all.

```
A P A N I P U R I Z X C V
B H E L P U R I Y U I O K
A S D J H A A L M U R I T
W E P H U C H K A E R T Y
E D V A D A P A V C V B N
D A B E L I V C W A P P R
S D L I T T I C H O K H A
C V B B H A J I Y A T G Y
V K A C H O R I E R T Y U
M O M O R Y U P A D D U Y
```

56

FESTIVE WHEEL

Can you guess the words hidden in these word wheels? They are all to do with festivals celebrated in India.

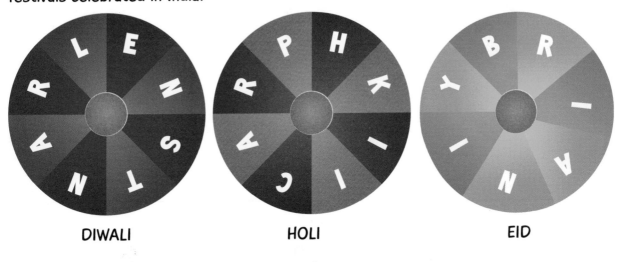

DIWALI

HOLI

EID

_____

_____

_____

AUTOGRAPH PLEASE

These famous Indians all have something in common with each other. Can you say what that is?

1. A R Rahman, Shankar, Ehsan, R D Burman are all _____

2. Prakash Padukone, Pulella Gopichand, P V Sindhu, Sania Nehwal are all

_____

3. Birju Maharaj, Mallika Sarabhai, Sonal Mansingh, Kanak Rele are all _____

4. Asha Bhonsle, Bombay Jayshri, Kishore Kumar, Mukesh are all _____

5. Kumar Mangalam Birla, Anil Ambani, Ratan Tata, Adi Godrej are all

_____

DANCE DANCE DANCE

How many of these dance forms can you identify?

_____   _____   _____

_____   _____   _____

_____   _____

BRIDAL SPLENDOUR

The name of a lovely sari that brides from Gujarat wear on their wedding day, is hidden in this puzzle. Can you find it?

H   H   O   R   C   G   A   L   A

DID YOU KNOW?

Let's see how many of these fun facts you know.

1. The first Indian to win an Oscar was _____.

2. The only cricketer to play for both India and England was _____.

3. The singer that legends say could cause rain by singing a rain raga, Megh Malhar, was called _____.

4. The lady who was called a human computer was _____.

5. India's first talkie movie was _____.

ANSWERS

page 4 MAKE A MATCH
Maharashtra—Mumbai; Gujarat—Gandhinagar; Goa—Panaji; Rajasthan—Jaipur; Uttarakhand— Dehradun, Madhya Pradesh—Bhopal; West Bengal—Kolkata

page 4 ROYAL TOUCH

C	H	A	N	D	R	A	G	U	P	T	A
S	D	B	W	E	R	S	W	E	R	T	K
R	T	U	D	C	F	H	X	C	B	B	B
B	G	R	H	R	J	O	W	S	A	D	A
S	D	F	G	H	T	K	C	F	B	G	R
X	M	S	H	I	V	A	J	I	U	Y	U
A	J	A	T	A	S	H	A	T	R	U	R
J	T	I	P	U	S	U	L	T	A	N	N
R	A	N	A	S	A	N	G	A	H	J	K

page 5 HIDE AND SEEK
avatar, chutney, shampoo, jungle, dacoit, bungalow, pyjama, loot, karma, chit

page 5 UNMASKED
C and F are identical.

page 6 MONUMENTAL CHECK
1. Agra, 2. Mamallapuram, 3. Mumbai, 4. Hyderabad, 5. Delhi, 6. Panaji

page 6 YUMMY MAZE

page 7 PICTURE MATCH
Diwali—diya; Eid—crescent moon; Gudi padwa—gudi; Christmas—tree; Bihu—dancer

page 7 FAMOUS FIVE
1. Milkha Singh, 2. Mary Kom, 3. Abhinav Bindra, 4. Rahul Dravid, 5. Sakshi Malik

page 8 STRUM AND HUM
1. flute, 2. nagara, 3. shehnai, 4. tabla, 5. jal tarang

page 9 SHADOW MATCH
I is the shadow

page 9 THAT'S ODD!
sari, cap, jeans, belt, anarkali

page 11 HELLO THERE
pranaam, vanakkam, namaste, nomoshkar, as-salam alaikum, kem cho, sat sri akaal, aadab, namaskaram

page 11 SMART CRAFT
Chanderi—saris, Kolhapuri—chappals, Madhubani—painting, Kondapalli—toys, Sankheda—furniture, Khurja—pottery

page 12 RIVER CHASE
1. Narmada, 2. Godavari, 3. Krishna, 4. Yamuna, 5. Jhelum

page 12 CRACK THE CODE
MAURYA

page 13 TWIN DANCERS
E and G are exactly alike.

page 13 SOMETHING'S ODD
Saina Nehwal, Medha Patkar, Yuvraj Singh, Karan Johar, Raja Ravi Varma

page 14 PERFECT PALINDROME
Malayalam

page 14 PUPPET ON A STRING

page 15 MONARCH MATCH
Gol Gumbaz—Sultan of Bijapur; Ashoka—Ashoka Stambh; Shivaji—Pratapgarh fort Mahal; Krishnaraja Wodeyar—Mysore Palace; Akbar—Agra fort; Queen of Jhansi—Gwalior fort

page 15 HIDDEN FOOD
Shrikhand

page 16 FESTIVE ROUTE

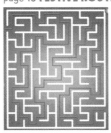

page 17 HIDDEN TRIBES

page 17 MELODY MAKERS
santoor, sarod, sarangi, tutari, mridangam

page 18 KATHAKALI MARVELS
H is different.

page 18 HIDDEN WORD
Here are some of the words you can form: rail, nail, nil, ail, ran, ark, lark, rank, rink, lair, akin

page 19 FARMER, WHAT DO YOU GROW?

C	O	T	T	O	N	A	E	D	C
S	M	A	I	Z	E	F	T	Y	U
E	R	T	Y	U	I	R	I	C	E
Z	X	C	V	B	A	J	R	A	V
R	A	G	I	A	S	D	F	G	H
E	D	R	J	O	W	A	R	R	T
W	W	H	E	A	T	C	V	F	G

page 19 WHAT'S THE SYMBOL?
1. peacock, 2. tiger, 3. lotus, 4. mango, 5. hockey, 6. banyan

page 20 NONSENSE WORDS
1. Sahyadri, 2. Himalayas, 3. Vindhyas, 4. Aravalli, 5. Nilgiri

page 22 FORT-I-FIED
Gwalior fort—Madhya Pradesh; Golconda Fort—Andhra Pradesh; Pratapgarh Fort—Maharashtra; Chittorgarh Fort—Rajasthan; Kangra Fort—Himachal Pradesh

page 22 FODDIE MAZE

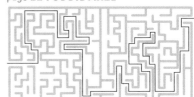

page 23 HAPPY HOLI-DAY

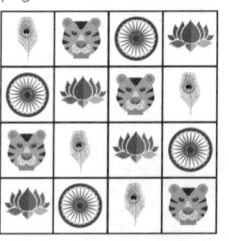

page 23 ODD FOOD

upma, sevayian, dosa, puran poli, kadhi

page 24 TRIBAL TRACT

A	N	G	A	M	I	A	L	E	D
J	W	E	R	T	Y	U	I	O	
A	A	S	D	F	U	A	S	U	R
N	W	W	E	R	N	W	R	F	T
T	S	C	V	B	D	A	D	F	G
I	B	A	N	J	A	R	A	B	G
A	D	E	T	Y	U	L	X	C	V
E	R	T	Y	B	H	I	L	E	R

page 24 HIDDEN WORD

1. pav, 2. bulb, 3. dam, 4. hat, 5. rub,
6. swarm

page 25 MISSING DANCER

1. Sikkim, 2. Indus, 3. Tamil Nadu,
4. Ahmedabad, 5. Rajasthan, 6. Assam
7. Delhi, 8. Elephanta, 9. Violin, 10. India
Answer: Sitara Devi

page 25 THE CLOTHING JUMBLE

mundu, ghagra, mekhla, achkan, pagri,
sari, dupatta, kameez

page 26 MISSING LETTERS

1. Haveli, 2. Chutney, 3. Bengaluru,
4. Ramayan, 5. Golconda, 6. Jharkhand

page 26 CODE CRACKERS

The East India Company

page 27 WHAT'S IN A NAME?

Bombay—Mumbai; Trivandrum—
Thiruvananthapuram; Baroda—Vadodara;
Calicut—Kozhikode; Coorg—Kodagu;
Madras—Chennai

page 27 WILD AND WONDERFUL

Across: 1. Mugger, 4. Tiger, 6. Hornbill,
8. Chittal, 9. Peacock, 10. Dugong
Down: 2. Gaur, 3. Rhinoceros, 5. Nilgai,
7. Leopard

page 28 HIDDEN WORD

Here are the words you can form: kit, hit,
lit, ail, talk, tail, hail, hilt, halt, hat

page 28 HAPPILY MARRIED

A and H are alike.

page 29 KIDDY WRITERS

1. Ruskin Bond, 2. Sudha Murthy 3. R K
Narayan 4. Anant Pai 5. Salman Rushdie

page 29 STUNNING SANCTUARIES

1. Uttarakhand, 2. Rajasthan,
3. Assam, 4. Karnataka, 5. Madhya
Pradesh, 6. West Bengal

page 31 THE HIDDEN EMPEROR

1. Bindusara, 2. Samudragupta,
3. Redfort, 4. Tipu Sultan, 5. Alexander,
6. Gayatridevi, 7. Razia Sultana,
8. Portuguese, 9. Bombay

Answer: Aurangzeb

page 32 SPOT THEM ALL

India Gate, Gateway of India, Qutb Minar,
Bulund Darvaza, Taj Mahal, Victoria
Memorial

page 32 SARI STYLE

1. West Bengal, 2. Gujarat, 3. Kerala,
4. Maharashtra, 5. Assam

page 33 CELEBRITY SPOTTING

1. Writing, 2. President of India,
3. Ornithologist, 4. Actor, 5. Singer

page 33 HIDDEN INSIDE

Here are some of the words you can form:
cap, lap, chap, help, pal, clap, leap, peal,
pale, help

page 34 LET'S GO CLASSICAL

1. Kuchipudi, 2. Odissi, 3. Sattriya
4. Kathak, 5. Bharatnatyam,
6. Kathakali, 7. Mohiniattam
8. Manipuri, Answer: Uday Shankar

page 35 SYMBOLIC SUDOKU

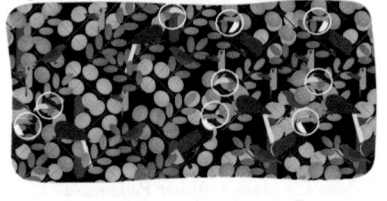

page 35 HIDDEN HORNBILLS

page 36 FINDITABAD

1. Hyderabad, 2. Ahmedabad,
3. Faridabad, 4. Secunderabad,
5. Aurangabad

page 36 MUGHAL SPLENDOUR

page 37 LANGUAGE LILTS

Bhojpuri—Bihar; Telugu—Andhra Pradesh,
Konkani—Goa; Awadhi—Uttar Pradesh;
Khasi—Assam

page 37 AMAZING ARTISTRY

Gujarat—Bandhani; Benaras—Benarsi;
Punjab—Phulkari; Andhra Pradesh—Ikat

page 38 STANDING STRONG

Bhimbetka—caves; Mahabodhi—temple;
Gingee—fort; Humayun's—tomb;
Falaknuma—palace

page 38 RICE IS NICE

idli, kheer, dosa, khichri, uttapam, pulao,
biryani

page 39 READY FOR A FEAST

IFTAR

page 39 MOVIE MAGIC

1. Lagaan, 2. Goopy Gyne Bagha Byne,
3. Mughal-e-Azam, 4. Raja Harishchandra,
5. Bhaag Milkha Bhaag

page 40 RICKSHAW RIDE

H is the shadow.

page 40 MAKING MUSIC

Chikara

page 41 FOLKSY FUN

Chholiya—Uttarakhand; Hojagiri—Tripura;
Karakattam—Tamil Nadu; Lavni—
Maharashtra; Dollu Kunitha—Karnataka

page 41 TRADITIONAL TRENDS

E is different.

page 42 FISHING FUN

Line 3

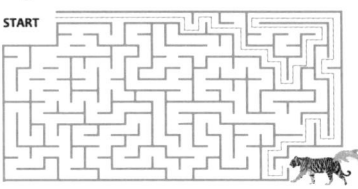